# SHADOW WORK JOURNAL AND WORKBOOK

*The Comprehensive Guide for Beginners to Uncover the Shadow Self & Become Whole as Your Authentic Self | Guided Prompts for Inner Child Soothing, Healing & Growth*

## 3 BOOKS IN 1

**Written by**

**Victoria Stevens**

# MASTER YOUR SHADOW

## 3 SHADOW WORK JOURNAL AND WORKBOOK IN 1

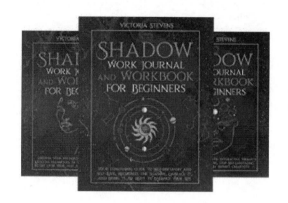

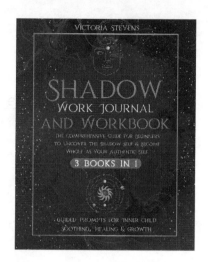

**+**

## GUILT AND SHAME

IN THE HEALING PROCESS OF TRAUMA AND FORGIVENESS. UNDERSTANDING THESE EMOTIONS AND HOW TO MOVE PAST THEM.

# VOICES OF SUPPORT WORLDWIDE FOR SHADOW WORK JOURNAL AND WORKBOOK

This book has changed my entire life. Combined with therapy it has addressed so many things. Thank you so much!!!!!
**- Christian A Cruz Cubero**

After two separate people at two different times within the same week told me about this workbook, and that it would change my life...I immediately grabbed it and was ready to do the work! Thank you for helping us all whose self-worth and self-esteem are not as high as everyone around us thinks they should be.
**- Denise Boucher Garofoli**

You owe it to yourself to grow into that beautiful butterfly you always dreamed of you are worth everything you desire and much more but sometimes you have to heal to bring your greatness to light that is what this book is about please buy it please put in the work because you know your definitely worth it.
**- Misty Ortiz**

It was well-written, the prompts were thought-provoking and there were plenty of deep dives included. That is what I was hoping for and that is what I got in this product. Highly recommend it to anyone looking to explore their shadows.
**- Rebecca Elaine Twiner**

I highly recommend this guided workbook to anyone seeking to heal their inner child and incorporate their shadow self. This workbook has been more valuable to me than years of therapy. Go at your own pace...take a break and come back to it. I can't recommend this enough.
**- Ness**

Since my best friend and I turned 30, we have had a lot of inner child wounds come to realization. We have let go of low-energy habits and trying to heal. This book was referred to us and just the beginning has helped us tremendously. We love the writing prompts.
**- Amber**

This book is a definite must. It makes you take a look at yourself and go within. Ask these deep questions that may trigger you but in a good way. How a word can bring up emotions and why they make you feel that way and how to work on it. I absolutely love it!!!

**- TC**

If you want to understand yourself or don't understand shadow work, this book is for you. It is also for you who is seasoned in shadow work but is lost and wants to find your way back slowly.

In my own words, shadow work is a way to rediscover yourself or understand yourself more. For one to understand the good, the bad, and the ugly in oneself, shadow work is one of the helpful " tools ". This book is like an ABC shadow workbook that can help.

The things I like about the book are that it's not only short but is packed with so much information in an easy way to understand. It's in parts; thus, one can take time to process the information and do the prompts. The guided prompts are also helpful as an "idea prompt" to guide you through the process.

The book itself is immense though it needs more space to journal all the thoughts. But one can always get a journal for that. It does, however, have space for you to write your own "idea prompts" so that is a good thing.

All in all, it helped me see my inner child and heal. I would recommend it to my family and friends.

**- Angela**

This book has been a revelation to me. It talks about a well-supported psychological theory regarding "the shadow" that each one of us carried around for most of our life without even knowing that it's there and wants to be taken into consideration for us to live an authentic life. It has made me think of my past and the effect of relevant people on me. It has helped me with putting things in the right perspective and clarified where I want to go from now on. I'm loving it. After all, "shadow work" is a psychotherapy method that can help you see through yourself clearly, come to terms with the past, and be able to move forward confidently. I particularly appreciated the 3 letters to yourself. Very clever exercise! Strongly recommended.

**- AC**

# WE'RE HERE BECAUSE OF YOU

If you have found any value in this material,
Please consider leaving a review and joining the Author's
Mission to bring more healing into this world
By scanning the QR-Code below ♥

Share a photo or video and write an honest review of your Shadow Work Journal and Workbook

on **Amazon, TikTok or Instagram** to get the new digital

book (pdf) on **"Shadow Work for Self-Love"**

**worth $19,99, absolutely free $0**

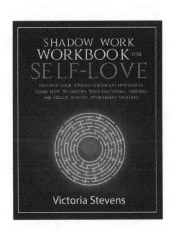

DM @yourshadowworks
email:

victoriastevens@yourshadowworks.com

with your link to receive your special
discount

*@yourshadowworks*

# The Oath

I, _____ in the face of past adversity and painful sensory experiences lived so far, hereby pledge to resolve what troubles my soul and to recognize, accept, and nurture my wounds.

I vow to be open to guidance and to complete the pages of this journal with commitment and self-compassion, embracing both the conscious and unconscious parts of my being.

I further recognize that living in space and time, as a Creation amongst other Creations, affects my collective destiny. As I heal myself, I heal my family, my community, and I release my ancestors.

I acknowledge to be accountable for my own happiness and fulfilment. As I bring my shadow to light, I bring more light into the world. Love, Joy, Peace and Abundance will manifest as a result.

My legacy to the world is to

_____

So, Be It!

Start Date_____

Signature _____

Completion Date_____

# TABLE OF CONTENTS

"A journey of a thousand miles begins with a single step" – Lao Tzu

# INTRODUCTION

Have you ever felt alone in your struggle? As if your voice is unheard in a sea of voices that drown you out. Are the voices sometimes your own? I'm sure you understand what I'm talking about. Trauma separates us from people in a way that makes us feel like we are looking through a window to the outside world. This book isn't here to cure your trauma or reverse what has happened to you; it is here to be your confidant and guide you through your personal path to wholeness, joyfulness, and give a sense of ease to your integrated self.

A companion to help you deal with the things that detach you from life. As someone who was verbally abused by her parents, I know how those feelings can work their way into your personal life. The worst part is that a moment where you feel fine can be turned into a moment where you lose control over your situational reactions, normally caused by internal triggers that project themselves on the parties involved in the interaction. There's a certain feeling that creeps up when we aren't quite sure who we are, and the overall human condition doesn't really allow the space to work through issues we might have.

From the moment we're born, we are classified in a preconceived label. If you're born with certain genitals, immediately you are an assumed gender and all decisions made about you up until a point becomes predetermined. It's people with their own struggles trying to predetermine our fates; moms who dream of daughters growing up to be wives, accompanied by fathers who live vicariously through their sons' sports careers. It's immediately put into this binary ideal, and while that's not a terrible thing, it can hinder the organic growth of a person.

You are under your parents' regime until you reach a certain age, by which you've already had their ideas and morals passed on to you. This system is what makes trauma such a disruptive force in our lives. See, we all have that "American Dream" in the back of our minds.

You know the sort: The perfect family, two kids and a dog, good careers, and a nice house one day. But when you are different, trapped, and someone who doesn't fit into that category, suddenly it's no longer good enough. Our minds 'other' us because we have been 'othered' by society. It's not a means to justify what has happened to you, in fact, it serves to confront the uncomfortable truth.

You don't need to be afraid because there are communities out there that share your pain and serve to help you. There are mental health professionals who are willing to work with you through everything you have dealt with. This workbook serves as your vent space, a safe space you can use to write your private thoughts and experiences down.

## Why Exercises with Writing Prompts?

"The more we become aware of our shadow the more personal power we hold, the less fear and anger we have towards others, and the less power difficult people have to set us off" - Prof. Steve Mortenson.

Journaling is one of the key suggested methods of shadow work because it forces you to get the shadow down on paper and expose its purest form. The shadow, after all, isn't an entity apart from you but instead a crucial piece of you. You aren't without your shadow, and by journaling and integrating it back into your being, you become your full self, and the shame of your past falls away, becoming experiences you can carry with you at all times. These prompts and questions are here to help you with your starting point in the journaling journey.

Journaling brings those hidden parts of ourselves to light, and when we record these psychological anomalies down in physical form, it becomes an easy source to reference for battling the intrusive insistence that we are not of value because of what we experienced in our younger days. It is there to keep you accountable as well. This process is not a leisure walk in the park.

Unfortunately, it is also there to help assist in keeping watch over your emotional and mental health. If I can use an example, it is a form of metamorphosis, and a crucial part of that process is to become a broken down metaphorical soup which is then rebuilt and reshaped to reveal a butterfly. Your components stay the same, but you are stepping back and reevaluating the person you are. Change is terrifying, but it is necessary, and the payoff, in the end, is worth it.

Writing it down also helps you take much-needed breaks, you can't do all of this in one night. By recording it, you create your endpoints so when you have had a rest from internal reflection, you know where you stopped and can recap your process up until then. Perhaps even after experiencing a few revelations, you can add to these notes on how your life, and maybe even your thought process, has already begun to change.

## Is This the Journey for You?

Over the years, society has developed in a way that forces us to hide from surrounding people on a day-to-day basis. It is not always strangers who see masked versions of us, sometimes it will even be our family members, friends, other significant people, or worse, ourselves. It is at that moment when you look at your hand and the imposter syndrome kicks in.

Our relationships have a large impact on us in the grand scheme of things. Those in our lives shape our lives, affecting our behavior. With Shadow Work, we can learn to combat our negative repressed feelings. These factors are all depending on our external environments often because of how people are ingrained to judge one another. Through the use of this workbook and journal, I hope it will be your fast companion on your journey to self-discovery and healing.

This workbook is the perfect self-help project for you to learn about the therapeutic method of Shadow Work. Using affirmations and writing prompts alongside well-researched information, the book motivates you to give the best possible objective outlook on how to work on your inner self. Most people grow up with some kind of early life trauma. It is highly possible you could have had an uneventful childhood that doesn't exempt us from developing a shadow self. We will go over those points later in the book, but for now, we will go over a detailed overview of what you, as the reader, can expect from your reading and journaling experience (Perry, 2015).

Over the course of this book, we will look at three parts of the Shadow Work journey. Through the use of different journaling methods, we will take a deeper look into the deep-seated shadow self that manifests itself at our lowest points and insecurities, which it takes and uses to disconnect us from ourselves. Almost no trauma is the same and every human experiences it in their own unique way.

There is a level of intensity that can occur, which doesn't diminish negative moments we might have experienced in the early developmental stage, as it is quite possible to gather small traumas throughout our lives. These little traumas may often occur at the hands of discrimination. Discrimination that usually affects people is often subjects such as homophobia, racism, sexism, or just general emotional and verbal abuse. Unfortunately, we can internalize almost every aspect of our past lives, later becoming rooted in emotional suppression. It is almost as if a rotten root has planted itself deeply into your emotional energy pool and is slowly but surely poisoning you from the inside out. We may even manifest it as hereditary features.

All these various factors can contribute to the metaphorical "big bad" that is our shadow, and in turn, create fear in us to confront the shadow. After all, who really enjoys rapid change? I know I don't, and that is why it is so important to nurture our internal selves. We don't want to end up lost and broken with no way out and no support system. As people, it is important to be honest with ourselves—once you take that step, the road will become easier to travel upon. This workbook will help you face the seemingly enormous task ahead and implement positive thinking towards your shadow. Especially since journaling is one of the vital steps in shadow work. Through the course of this book, we will explore themes and delve into information that will benefit that with which you struggle. I will break it up into three parts that will explore the demons that plague us.

You don't have to be a writer to write about your personal experiences. The goal is to encourage visible growth and give you a way to view your progress. Take a deep breath and realize that you are safe. This book shall be your companion throughout your healing journey. Remember to be honest with yourself.

Writing Prompts: Who Are You?

I thought I would use this chapter as a means to introduce you to the writing format we will follow throughout the journal. It will include an affirmation to help you center your thoughts, as well as an image to reflect on. This is all part of the story you will be creating as you go along.

## Date:

1. Who are you?

2. What is your current occupation?

3. Who are the people in your life who mean the most to you?

4. Do you have any pets, if so, what are their names?

5. What is your current age?

6. Are you excited about this journaling experience?

7. If you're nervous or scared, write some of your concerns.

8. What do you want to get out of the experience, and which places in your life are you ready to tackle?

# Writing Prompts: Who Are You?

# Writing Prompts: Who Are You?

# Writing Prompts: Who Are You?

# Writing Prompts: Who Are You?

"Until you make the unconscious, conscious, it will direct your life and you will call it fate," - Carl Jung

# PART ONE:
# SELF-DISCOVERY AND SELF-ACCEPTANCE

When we think about self-love and internal reflection, it easily becomes a very uncomfortable thought; after all, we humans are oftentimes controlled by our insecurities and feelings of uneasiness because we do not want to be in a mind space shared with the whole of our personality and our archetype. Subsequently, if we have hidden parts of ourselves over the years because they were classified as bad or not addressed by outside sources, how can we then expect to sit comfortably next to our inner self at the mental dinner table? These negative parts tend to manifest outwardly without us even noticing, and sometimes by the time we become aware, it's too late and the relationships around us have already started cracking. We manifest these insecurities into defensive fear that makes us react or act negatively towards our relationships.

These issues include toxic behaviors such as codependency, infidelity, or even unintentional gaslighting; all things that directly affect our relationships. However, relationships aren't the only things that get affected by these shortfalls in our emotional intelligence; they can also heavily affect our work life and everyday tasks. For example, if you're someone with anxiety, you know how quickly the snowball effect takes place. A small insignificant task can turn our whole lives around and hinder progress just like that. Maybe you have an important meeting coming up with your boss, and because you're caught up on impressing him and avoiding judgment and rejection, you hyper-fixate on the situation and it becomes this insistent thought as if it's a mosquito and refuses to go away and let you be.

This meeting starts to slowly pester you and your brain enters fight or flight mode. Now, suddenly you can't sleep, or you sleep too much and can't eat, or you eat too much. Regardless it builds and builds, and builds, and then the morning before your meeting, you run out of coffee, and that becomes the end of the world because why can't anything go right in your life? This thought process is a consequence of a lack of self-actualization, and if there is no moment where you stop to evaluate your actions, it won't get any easier.

I understand that facing a mistake or moment of weakness can be a shameful experience, but this book is here to assist in your journey and give you the tools to learn and understand that you do not need to live with shame or fear of the person you truly are. We are all human, and we all have our stories and complexities to tell. You have a story, and it's time for you to unlock that side within you. What most people don't realize is that psychological problems can have a massive impact on your physical health.

While it's not a cure-all, it is a symptom reliever. It still takes energy to improve your health, and when the mind is drained, it is near impossible to muster up the willpower to fight. Emotional energy is oftentimes a missing variable in the recipe for healing, along with emotional intelligence. Your brain might not affect every single aspect of your body and its reactions but it does send fight or flight signals where they aren't needed, this extra shot of unnecessary adrenaline can be problematic in our lives. That's normally the effect trauma has on us, putting your mind in constant alert mode and turning it into exhaustion.

It's the suppressed emotions that prevent us from moving on with our lives because they keep subconsciously poking the bear. In part one, we will be going over the basics of Shadow Work, the shadow, and its origin, using this information to start the personal journey towards confidence and healing. It's useful to understand why a shadow manifests in our conscious minds and how we as individuals can confront that part of us.

# What is the Shadow?

"Part of every misery is, so to speak, the misery's shadow or reflection: The fact that you don't merely suffer but have to keep on thinking about the fact that you suffer. I not only live each endless day in grief but live each day thinking about living each day in grief," - C.S Lewis.

On July 26, 1875, in Kesswil, Switzerland, a man was born who fathered the first beginnings of analytic psychology and expanded on Sigmund Freud's approach and theories to psychoanalysis (Fordham & Michael S.M. Fordham, 2019). This man was Carl Gustav Jung. By definition, psychoanalysis is the practice by which theories on therapeutic methods take place and deal with the unconscious mind. It is a studied technique that elevates symptoms of mental illness and disorders and serves to bring relief to the symptoms that haunt the people controlled by them. These methods bring repressed fears and memories forward to the conscious mind and can use techniques such as dream interpretation to expose subconscious thought. Unlike Sigmund, however, Jung believed that people aren't as simple as previously thought. Where Sigmund pushed for the idea that people develop a psychosexual persona at an early stage in their childhood and that all behavior after that is based upon these primate instincts, Jung pushed for a more complex human nature that thrives with conflicts and feelings. He theorized and expanded upon the idea that we have an unconscious "conscious mind" made up of events that shaped us as children. Much like Freud, he agreed we are inherently shaped in our early developmental phase and that most things we experience during this period will manifest in one way or another. This could be negative habits like drug use, paranoia, abusive traits towards others, or it could be moral behaviors such as compassion and the need to help people regardless of who they are. He realized that as children, we experienced many things on the surface because we could not yet properly understand and organize the things we were told. This is why the brain tucks it away and leaves it in a symbolic "hoarders pile" for us to sort out later as our brains develop and our emotional understanding strengthens. Jung was also one of the first psychiatrists that pioneered the idea of personality archetypes and the concepts behind introversion and extraversion. He takes a look at how you were raised, and then bases that study on your outward behavior towards people. He is the man we can thank for the test that determines which personality quadrant we fall in. It's a bit more complicated than those tests that classify you as quirky, usually used by schools and workplaces to test a person's aptitude for a job. Those personas are what he called the collective unconscious, and they kind of push the buttons of our responsive states. He was a prominent figure in his field from early on, having even been associated with Freud, and even though they disagreed later on in their respective careers, he drew some influence from the nature versus nurture theory. Many of our current habits are usually due to direct authoritative influences we had as children, the principal source of contempt usually a parent/guardian/caretaker who wasn't as conscious about their issues and imparted that on us, sometimes unintentionally and other times maliciously.

You saw me mention archetypes, and I bet you're wondering what they are, exactly? How do they influence us as people? Well, he theorized that there were almost 12 archetypes, but this book focuses primarily on three. I just wanted to use this moment to list them off so you can get a brief understanding about why they exist and why they are important to be aware of.

There is the persona, which I have used a lot in the text, the mask that you wear when interacting with the outside world. The unconscious mind that lays beneath the surface is the one that influences the way it presents itself to people. You've felt it before, how you become a fragment of your true self around people. I know I have done this too, where I have kept certain people at a distance and others closer. Where I shared a certain set of opinions with a select group of people exclusively and withheld other opinions from people who I know will respond unpleasantly. That is the persona I present when I'd prefer to stay non-confronting. It's not a bad thing, it could be, but it's necessary for us. We need that ability to adapt to our environments, especially when we are in a high-stress space. The last thing you want to do is let the full spectrum of your emotions loose. It's all situational in the end. Then there is the shadow, which is self-explanatory, and we will dedicate an entire chapter to its existence, so I will move on from the shadow and jump right into the next phase of your inner workings: The Animus, the true self in the sense of who we are on a primal level. It's the biggest source of our collective unconscious and helps us to communicate our outward feelings. The animus is imaged by Jung as being female in body, male in psyche, and involves itself in our sexual expression.

Here, we develop our gender identities and discover our preferences. We are normally born with our animus, so unlike the shadow, it's not something that gets shaped over time, but has already become a shape. It's already there, just waiting to be discovered. An animus can be separated from itself, but once it's been accepted in its most primal form, you will have freedom. It can also be slightly influenceable by what is often floating around in our personal consciousness, be wary of that. Finally, we have the Self, the ego. While we hide it behind all our other archetypes, this aspect is considered key. I don't have a chapter dedicated to the ego, and frankly, I think that is a book all its own. The ego is you, your individualism, represents unity, and is the center of it all. Think of the ego as the sun and the rest of you as the solar system. It's the voice that seems so far away in the back of our mind, trying to steer you towards conflicts that need resolution. It is the part of you that is you, and when there is chaos and disagreement between your archetypes, the ego can easily fall away and become small and unimportant, meaning sometimes it acts out because you're not giving it attention. I'll mention the ego periodically in this book while also referring to its other name, which is self. Usually when you act out of character there is no synergy between the parts that make you. The ego is supposed to be the leader and director, but when it's been diminished, its voice barely reaches the top of the conscious food chain. Don't worry, we will unify them all soon and bring order to your chaos (Owings, 2020).

For a fun side note, here are some additional archetypes of Jung that have been used in a very famous aptitude test system, and some of their qualities that you can fall into. These categories aren't set in stone, and depending on where you are in your life, the results can vary. When you have time, I highly recommend you take the Jung typology test and write down your results (Jung Personality test, 2019). Out of all the personality tests, it's still seen as the most accurate one. A nice prompt would also be to make a mask based on your results; a visual representation of who you could be (Neill, 2018).

### 1. The Caregiver:

The one who nurtures, usually the one who supports the others, presents traits such as selflessness, loyalty, and doesn't always focus on their own well-being. Incredibly relatable.

### 2. The Innocent:

Alternatively known as the child, exemplifies kindness, naivety, creativity, and vulnerability.

### 3. The Hero:

Ready for challenges and is all about perseverance, discipline, and can come across as arrogant. The protagonist's center of attention.

### 4. The Explorer:

All about self-improvement and looking for the next challenge. Can be unreliable and don't like conformity.

### 5. The Creator:

Projects creativity and is a visionist. Can be aloof, idealistic, and sometimes lack the discipline to be practical.

### 6. The Lover:

Intimate, passionate, and full of unadulterated love. There to offer support but can also be slightly irrational sometimes.

### 7. The Sage:

The sage is strategic and uses intelligence to observe situations. Tied to wisdom and being mentors, their weakness can be apprehension towards risks.

### 8. The Jester:

As per the name, the jester is the funny and charming one. Can be insightful, but it's in contrast to the ability to be obnoxious.

### 9. The Everyman:

Non-gendered and advocates equality, includes all people into this category. Wants to connect with others and is the sort that easily stands out. Usually lack the ability to foresee future events and can be unprepared.

### 10. The Ruler:

All about status and being successful. It wants control. This can be a double-edged sword as the need for control throws off their ability to delegate.

### 11. The Outlaw:

Rebel without a cause, independent, and rejects society's terms and conditions. Can be quite narcissistic and sometimes involved in illegal activity.

### 12. The Magician:

Finally, the magician likens to that of an inventor and dreamer. Obsessed with the universe and the laws that bind it. Sometimes they can be manipulators and their carelessness can lead to negative consequences.

According to observations made by Jung, he noticed that people often had illogical responses to certain words because of an unconscious emotional stimulus they received when hearing words they were uncomfortable with. As an example, in conservative and religious communities, there is an aversion to words or conversations surrounding that of a sexual nature, usually because of the way authority figures of that particular group of people implement an illusion of a high moral standard. This high moral standard is usually so impossible to reach that it can cause children to become anxiety-driven and impart in them a deep-rooted sense of validation seeking because 'good' behavior gets rewarded and 'bad' behavior doesn't. It's unfortunate because most people just parrot the rules they had grown up with. This lack of questioning and reflection can stunt useful growth more than they, or you, even realize.

The children who grow up in that environment then go on to also sub-consciously parrot the information they received to their children, and so on and so forth, creating this vicious cycle. Unless there is a total determination to reject the very ideals we grew up with, the odds of us still doing things we learned from our parents are high. If you want to break the cycle, do it. Don't let fear stop you from becoming the best version of yourself today. That doesn't mean you have to entirely deviate from the ideals you were raised with, but if something that you are carrying around as baggage is keeping you from being the person you need to be, then it's time to reevaluate who you are and where you're going. If you have a loud family and have a significant other in your life that is normally quiet and reserved, you'll quickly notice how much that affects your relationship.

Opposites attract, but that doesn't mean there aren't clashing issues underneath the surface, which is easily true when people bring up compatibility. I think that's quite a good analogy. We aren't always compatible with our shadow, which will be explored in the next chapter, but what many people seem to get wrong about compatibility is that it means the parties involved need to be the same. I find this sentiment a tad bit misleading. Think of a jigsaw; no piece is the same, and yet they fit together and create a beautiful picture. Right now, before your integration period, you are this half-built puzzle with scattered pieces. With the book, you will slowly start to organize your pieces, identify them, and finish the masterpiece that is already lurking there.

This is exactly why self-reflection is so important, and while it can be extremely daunting, you can gain the confidence to push for that compatibility with your entire self, eventually becoming comfortable enough to express it towards others. With reflection comes understanding, and with understanding comes acceptance. It's what we want, isn't it? To simply be.

At this point, you might review all this information and feel a bit overwhelmed. After all, what do Carl Jung and Sigmund Freud have to do with shadow work, and why am I calling you a puzzle? What does this have to do with understanding your shadow? Let me clarify: Each person has their own shadow that develops in the subconscious mind. Jung really wanted people to understand this fact. The shadow, in simple terms, is a personification of complex emotions we can't easily process. As mentioned before, as children, we could only understand things on a superficial level, and in turn, all experiences difficult to process, like traumatic experiences and negative events, get compartmentalized and mashed together in the shape of our personal shadow. Normally, we see a shadow as bad because it's dark and evil in most media, but at its core, a shadow is just a mirrored version of you that mimics you. I think the shadow gets a bad rap and so did Carl Jung.

We tend to demonize the parts of us that people make us feel ashamed of, and that turns the shadow into this monster. It's like that moment when you are alone in your dark room, and the jacket hung over a chair looks like that creature from the deep come to eat you, but the minute the light flickers on, we're relieved to realize it was nothing to fear. Abstract thought is great, but at some point, it needs to take form, and that is why we refer to the 'dark' part of ourselves as the shadow.

The shadow is created from childhood experiences and normally represents our darkest, hidden personality traits. It takes everything negative in our life and inherently embodies it, becoming a mirror reflection of self to our external appearance towards our everyday environments. Many people reject this part of themselves because confronting the shadow often makes people quite uncomfortable and can provide a sense of fear and apprehension in their daily lives. The shadow becomes the part of you that you refuse to acknowledge in the mirror, that tiny dose of self-loathing we tend to suppress as far as possible in our minds. Think of the shadow as your emotional punching bag.

# Writing Prompts:
## Discovery

Take the time and really sit with this prompt. Its goal is to discover what the areas in your life are that have started to be affected by your outside persona. Remember to add your own personal mantra in the open spaces.

## Date:

1. When you look at other people around you, which traits appeal to you the most?

2. Which aspects of your life are you hoping to improve upon?

3. What makes you feel embarrassed, and what negative emotions do you feel are better avoided?

4. What is it about yourself that you dislike? If you could change one feature, what would that be?

5. What's the meanest thing someone has said to you in the past?

6. What do you think your shadow is made of?

7. Describe a moment in recent times that have made you feel unsafe.

8. Why do you think you felt that way?

9. Do you lie to people about how you feel? What is the feeling you lie about the most?

10. Is there anything in your life that you are afraid of messing up?

11. What is it? How do you think you can tackle the situation?

12. Close off the page with a quick overview of what you have written and highlight bits where you want to put most of your focus.

# Writing Prompts: Discovery

# Writing Prompts: Discovery

# Writing Prompts: Discovery

# Writing Prompts: Discovery

*Affirmation:* I am unique, and the faults that I see in myself are a representation of something deeper within me. I am going to be alright. I am beautiful and very extraordinary.

# How the Shadow is Created

"Like a shadow, I am and I am not," - Rumi.

As mentioned before, we create the shadow subconsciously and its manifestations can become quite intentional and physical. What usually happens after it's formed is that we only notice its existence in times that make us feel confined within the shackles of the mind. It usually tends to present itself in moments where we feel unfulfilled, and the trajectory of our lives causes us great unhappiness. A terrifying idea, since it seems to demand our attention. However, there is no need to panic. The shadow isn't some supernatural force that takes over you, possesses your body, and takes involuntary actions.

In this journey, it will become clear that the shadow might feel like a hated enemy who works against you. It is actually a love letter created by your mind in order to protect you from its best capabilities. While this is sometimes too protective, it's actually your friend. When you take the opportunity to 'sit' down with your shadow, you will see it has your best interests at heart. After all, it is you, and who knows you better than yourself? Jung widely believed that making your shadow a bad guy was a misrepresentation of its intentions.

While we view the shadow as a metaphorical embodiment of our worst traits, the sort of traits we 'other' from our dominant personality, it is actually a much more complex entity than that. I'd argue that what Jung intends to indicate is that the shadow is a blanket weaved in order to protect the fragile person inside. In part two, we will explore the small child hiding inside of all of us, but the basic concept is that the shadow is more of an overactive protector of our emotions. The trauma we retain throughout our adult life never really goes away, which is why the shadow manifests itself, oftentimes encouraging poor behavior in us, such as addictions or the incentive to hurt those surrounding us.

This need to hide your vulnerabilities behind a mask doesn't make you a bad person, though. There isn't a black and white with people, and though it seems blurred when the shadow is making noise, you are just a human being like the rest of us who deserves to give yourself compassion so that others can receive it too. All people are susceptible to the shadow, and what tends to happen is we see other people's shadows, that sometimes seem better or worse managed than ours, and usually we don't want to face our own because of these superficial assumptions. This is usually because as we reach adulthood, traits get sorted by society into being good or bad without any input from us.

Even things as simple as what we wear get inherently judged by society, making us feel like we are boxed in when our individual expression is robbed from us. We should all keep on striving for individualism. It's not an easy battle, but when the smoke clears, it serves to make you stronger and more confident in yourself. Maybe the lack of choice and control is what creates that aversion to the shadow since we project what society has projected on us on the shadow, the fear of losing control and being judged overpowering our need to validate and love ourselves, and not seek that validation and love solely from those around us.

We like to suppress these parts because we wish for them to go away. They won't go away, and they won't heal on their own; they leave scars, and even scabs need doctoring. The smallest of injuries can become an infection, so it needs to be treated and attended to before it kills us. Packing these issues away in the darkest parts of our minds just creates a problem for later in our lives and can cause problems that we don't always know how to face. To recap, because the shadow is created by repressing our most sensitive natures, it shows that there can be negative and positive connotations to it. It takes shape over the course of a few years and rarely shows itself in an instant when we are younger. As children, we lack the emotional maturity to acknowledge its existence. As adults, we know, because of society's expectations, that anything that reflects badly on us is to be shut away and never talked about or confronted. All these factors work together to create the shadow, and in turn, hurt us.

Reflections

This prompt should help you start to get a basic understanding of the origins of your own shadow self and give you an introduction to its presence. Remember to answer these questions honestly, and don't be afraid to dive deep within yourself to unlock the past. Be caring, open-minded, and compassionate. Center yourself before answering any of these questions, as you need to be in a safe environment in order to tackle the shadow and the love you need to generate towards it and yourself.

## Date:

1. What were you like as a child?

2. What were your hopes and dreams?

3. Who were your parents/guardians/caretakers and what were their values?

4. What traits did they have that you hoped you didn't have?

5. What is one thing you're afraid of because of the authority figures in your life?

6. Take a moment and separate traits of your parents/guardians/caretakers into two categories: Bad and good. Which ones do you

resonate with the most, and how do they impact your daily life?

7. How has this reflected upon your shadow?

8. If you could say one thing to the shadow, what would it be?

9. If it's a negative feeling, how can you reiterate that into something positive and compassionate?

10. If the shadow has recently given you grief, can you find a reason to forgive it?

11. What would you like to be known for?

12. Finish this chapter by reflecting on your answers and making a list of the most important people in your life, using one word to describe their influence on you. This activity will be used later in the integration part of the book to help come to terms

with those who will be your support system and those who you will put at a distance.

# Writing Prompts: Reflection

# Writing Prompts: Reflection

# Writing Prompts: Reflection

# Writing Prompts: Reflection

Affirmation: What I say matters, and as I deserve kindness, so does the shadow within me. I will love and respect myself alongside the shadow because I am worthy.

# The Problem with the Shadow

"Unless we do conscious work on it, the shadow is almost always projected: That is, it is neatly laid on someone or something else, so we do not have to take responsibility for it," - Robert Johnson.

Now that we understand the basis of the shadow and its creation, I think it's important to elaborate on what problems the shadow can manifest in your life. I've mentioned our relationships before and how the shadows can influence our reactions to the people in our lives. These are the unfortunate symptoms of a segregated sense of self. The goal here is to take these internal problems you might have and integrate them so you can become that masterpiece I mentioned before. The shadow can cause lots of difficulties in our everyday lives and many people call these thoughts borderline parasitical, a leech that absorbs the light into an endless hungry void. However, as Jung stated, our animosity towards the shadow is not to our benefit. Calling it a parasite is too harsh, but this comes with the innate defense mechanism towards vulnerability. Often it can feel as if we are letting ourselves get exposed, as if we stand naked in front of a crowd, and it's a big exhibit of our worst sides. A typical scenario would be when we let our insecurity about something lash out towards someone we care about, or even in our professional life.

When we struggle to come to terms with this reality, our shadow self can cause a rationalization that causes emotional pain towards others, and while the reaction isn't always invalid, it takes a mature person to realize that sometimes we act a certain way because somewhere deep down we are hurting, and an unresolved hurt can be dangerous to our personal lives. An example that can be used for this scenario is that if you experience intense verbal abuse and are subject to emotional degradation, you tend to take commentary of people very personally, meaning you are prone to impulsive decisions. If you had parents who barely gave you financial freedom, odds are that you might end up becoming addicted to spending. Oftentimes, things you lacked as a child get pushed to the extreme when you reach adulthood.

Drugs, alcohol, and other addictive substances can also become a crutch that you lean on to distract from your internal struggles. These shadow 'manifestations' of you will project itself in many ways that I'd like to go over with you so that when you do journal, it will be easy to take note of. Remember, the shadow isn't just a personality but a projection of our inner being. Projections happen when our awareness of behavior gets pushed outside of our immediate consciousness. Since our shadow is an accumulation of your rejected qualities, they become an automatic filler for your opinion on people around you. These thoughts and feelings give you an assumed perception of people. We will learn more about acceptance and integration later in the book, which will hopefully shine a light on your struggles. We want to take the negative projection and twist that to the positive projection.

Projections

Our projections are a manifestation of what happens internally. Use these next few prompts to take a look at your outward behavior and try to gauge just how much your emotions have reflected on other people.

## Date:

1. Does the way you treat other people reflect how you treat yourself?

2. What usually triggers your feelings of insecurity?

3. What sort of things have people said towards you that have affected you deeply, and how do you react to their words?

4. Are you content with your relationships? Is there anything about them you wish to change? Even if it's positive.

5. When certain subjects are brought up between you and people in your life, do you find yourself setting up a wall to avoid getting overwhelmed?

6. When you have this wall up, how difficult is it for people to get past it and why do you keep it up.

7. Which people in your life are causing this reaction and what are their similarities to people you've had around you in the past?

8. Is it a fair reason to put up a wall? Or are you protected by fear of getting hurt?

9. What are you afraid of?

10. What is it that you want to be appreciated for?

11. Is there anything in your life that feels as though people are neglecting it?

12. Take a moment to finish off this chapter by writing a quick reflective piece about your answers.

# Writing Prompts: Projections

# Writing Prompts: Projections

# Writing Prompts: Projections

*Affirmation: If I notice and understand my shadow, I will understand the surrounding people.*

# How to Recognize the Shadow Within You

"Carl Jung called this his shadow work. He said we never see others. Instead, we see only aspects of ourselves that fall over them. Shadows. Projections. Our associations," - Chuck Palaniuk, Diary.

The symptoms of a repressed and bad shadow relationship include behavioral patterns and external projections, such as getting triggered by people and their behaviors towards us, especially when they do something that unintentionally offends us. While offending us isn't acceptable behavior, when we suppress our shadow, we deal with it in a way that is detrimental to our personal growth, implementing unhealthy patterns in our behavior. Learning internal acceptance encourages compassion towards ourselves and ultimately to outside parties.

Another symptom of the shadow self is that we also become people pleasers. We become so afraid of disappointing those around us that we hide our own truths from them and tend to say yes to requests we would rather not have agreed to. This behavior is often a throwback to our childhood and can be connected to how we were raised around our parents. For example, children who had parents that put an extensive amount of academic pressure on them can often grow up to become overachievers and develop anxiety disorders.

There are few more symptoms of a shadow self, including, but are not limited to:

- Criticizing and judging other people who do not comply with the "social norm" and act freely in the way they express themselves

- When you feel judged, or as if people are watching your every move, that normally derives from insecurity created by the shadow self.

- Emotional triggers, such as things that upset us on a deep level.

- Possible feelings of overwhelming anxiety and fear, sometimes your shadow self, create a feeling of imposter syndrome. Where you feel as if you're constantly on the verge of being "caught out."

- Emotional indifference is also a symptom of a shadow self-hiding beneath the surface. We usually take negative experiences and pack them away as a form of dealing with trauma. In turn, creating the automatic reaction to intense emotional situations with a lack of reaction, which is bad because that means we will only experience the accumulated emotions at a later, unexpected date.

Symptoms

Use this prompt as an opportunity to reflect upon how you have treated others and yourself as a direct result of the shadow and its subconscious influence on you. Jung said this sort of interaction with yourself is crucial. Don't forget your breath and breathing to stay calm.

## Date:

1. How do you think people perceive you?

2. Who has the most influence over you, and how does that affect your actions?

3. In what way would you describe your personality type?

4. What frightens and triggers you the most about people?

5. Do you feel people have misconceptions about you, if so, why do you think that is?

6. When have you been self-destructive in your life and what was usually the reason?

7. What do you judge the most about yourself and other people?

8. Reflect on your friendships and categorize them via who makes you feel the safest and most secure.

9.  If you could write a note/letter to the people in your life, what would you want to tell them?

10. Are there certain types of people that make you uncomfortable?

11. What habits have you picked up over the years that you would like resolved?

12. Do you use the habits as a form of coping, or to detach from those around you?

# Writing Prompts: Symptoms

# Writing Prompts: Symptoms

# Writing Prompts: Symptoms

# Writing Prompts: Symptoms

*Affirmation: I will perceive myself with compassion and love.*

"The more you are able to face the pain you experience, the more capable you become,"
– Joan Rosenberg.

# *Bringing the Shadow to Light*

You've learned about a few results of a suppressed shadow, meaning it's time to delve into the confrontation as part of the shadow. It's a crucial step in the art of shadow work and will help you move on with your life and get a deeper understanding of the things plaguing your personal life, relationships, and work balance. But why confront and trigger your shadow, you ask? Wouldn't it be better to instead avoid the messy situation of triggering negative emotions from your early childhood? Healthy triggers aren't impossible, and in fact, should be encouraged. Only when we start unpacking the shadow and its behavior will we learn to live and let it live. It is like unclogging a pipe and having free flow again, but a pipe can't be unclogged without a plumber and a manual to the tools necessary.

In the next chapter, we will go over how to trigger, confront, and develop a healthy relationship with your shadow. There will be a few affirmations and prompts to help you get started on your internal dialogue with the shadow. The goal of bringing the shadow into the light and out of its slumber is for one key factor, integration. Integration is a crucial part of self-love and learning to accept yourself fully. By integrating the shadow, you will be creating an assimilated mental ecosystem in your body and mind, which in turn will help you with clear focus throughout your days. It's a method to relieve any anxiety you might be feeling about yourself.

The consequences of letting your shadow stay in the dark can be things such as anxiety, depression, and picking up bad habits. We do things to circumvent the void in our personal abyss, using distractions to avoid the genuine issue. All these things become crutches to feel quick moments of happiness.

How do we confront the shadow, and where do we start? It is important to center yourself before attempting any sort of triggering behavior. You want to be as comfortable and open-minded as possible to avoid major total negative regression into a headspace that encourages destructive behavior traits. You are the only one who knows your limits, and while it is important to push and challenge these limits; it is also important to acknowledge your limits and then make the decision to set a space up where you can converse and challenge our shadow's preconceived shape.

### Introspection

- Find a space, it can be your room or the living room—maybe even put on some soothing music in the background and center your mind to feel at ease with the preparation to explore your repressed psyche. It will be important to have a journaling space near you so that you can document your progress, which is an excellent tool for personal reflection later on.

- After you have created the confrontation space, it is time to approach the shadow with an open mind and full honesty. The point of triggering its reactive responses is so that you can look at those "ugly parts," or yourself, and accept them unconditionally. Take the negative bits about yourself and inspect them. Reject the input of your inner critic, open the wounds, and expose the raw parts of your psyche.

- Start asking yourself tough questions, ones that make your insides squirm—think of regrets you have or a moment in your life where the power was taken from you. Take that power back and answer the questions with total transparency.

- Naturally, through this process, you should eventually enter the phase of childhood reflection and start going over the events that have led you up to your current state, which will often be painful and create a sense of fear, and I know from personal experience, regresses you back to your most vulnerable state. It is important to give that inner child a hug and assure them they are safe here.

- In this state, you can start asking questions such as, was I completely accepted? What was expected of me? Was it realistic, and what emotional reactions were seen and judged by those around you, especially your parents?

- As you start to ask these questions and eventually transition into answering them, you will realize that these new behaviors and total courageous honesty cultivate a sense of relief in you, which leads to self-love and acceptance. As you get to know your shadow self, you realize that a lot of your behavior can be explained, and in turn, ratified. Knowing is the first step to healing.

A Letter to Yourself

Use the space to write a letter to your current self, detailing everything you are going through and feeling right now at this moment. You will use this to look back on later in your life as a way to record and manage your growth as a person. Make sure you enforce empathy towards yourself, even when you are writing negatively. In the long run, this will only enforce self-love. This prompt is the chance to expand on the things that are giving you joy, that is giving you grief, and what your present life balance is like. Is your boss giving you trouble? Do you have a promotion that's making you nervous and you're not sure if you're up to the job? Are you having problems with your friends and family? These are all small thoughts you can think about. If I can use an example of my own writing, I like to use the space to study my behaviors and reaction to people around me in order to know where my high-risk areas are. If a coworker has upset me, I will start off a passage about how they reacted, how it upset me, analyze why I reacted the way I did, and then I will try and understand why they might have upset me.

You don't have to use this direct formula, but you can use that kind of thought process when writing about yourself. If you want to focus on your outward appearance, you can also do that by taking a look in the mirror and noting the nice parts about your looks and the parts you see as unpleasant. Another thing I like to do is insert myself in a parable of sorts, so some creative writing. If you want your letters to flow, maybe even create a fairytale and represent the three phases you are going through. Your beginning, your middle, and your end. There's no right or wrong with how your letter is structured, just so long as it tells a reflective story that you can read about yourself.

# Date:

## Writing Prompts: A letter to yourself

# Writing Prompts: A letter to yourself

# Writing Prompts: A letter to yourself

# Writing Prompts: A letter to yourself

"Anything that is 'wrong' with you began as a survival mechanism in childhood,"
– Dr.Gabor Matè

# PART TWO:
# THE INNER CHILD

Now that you have been informed about the shadow, it's time to realize that it's not your only unconscious persona hiding beneath the surface. This next part is to introduce you to your inner child; a joyful, curious part of you that builds upon wonder in your life. The child is the one that makes you braver and stronger; it helps boost your self-esteem and encourages that confidence we often lack in our lives. It is all about your inner child and who it is. If you've experienced trauma in your life, it's possible that your child is wounded, which could be why you struggle to build up that confidence and need to accept yourself fully. So, I'd say the shadow is normally a blanket or protective defense mechanism you have subconsciously created to fight against the fear and shame that usually surrounds the traumatic events in your life. The child is the part of you who wishes to run free. Normally, this child comes out in moments when you do something that is often seen as childlike. When the shadow remains unresolved, we tend to package these mannerisms as shameful, hence punishing the child for just expressing itself, which is never an advisable thing to do. With the shadow there to 'protect' the inner child from negative feelings, it ends up hurting the child, often regurgitating behaviors it learned when you were a child. It becomes a metaphorical parent with what you used to express yourself in your daily life.

Letting the shadow become this protector might sound like the right idea at first, but it's actually not always a good thing since the shadow hides our inner child, meaning parts of us that used to be filled with wonder and dreams. The creative and intuitive parts of us are hidden away even more so than the shadow, ending up unintentionally stifling the joy we feel over small, good things and that can end up causing us depression and lack of motivation. In the next few chapters, we will go over how the inner child is found, and how to reach the emotional intelligence needed to become your inner child's nurturer. We want to explore the links between the inner child, codependency, and toxic relationships formed because of how the shadow covers up the good parts of our inner child, accumulating to a greater understanding of self.

# What is the Inner Child?

"Hold the hand of the child that lives in your soul. For this child, nothing is impossible," - Paulo Coelho.

When you peel back the layers and layers of the shadow, at some point you will reach the inner child; a personality archetype that is formed in the unconscious mind and holds the key to our ability to dream. In this part of ourselves, we enact, with imaginative vigor, our unmet needs. It's essentially the part of our mind where we dream and encourage imagination. There can also lie bits of a repressed childhood, especially if they did not give us the chance to really live that carefree life. Quite a few people who were forced to grow up too fast have expressed their loss at what they see as happiness because children are still naïve and can't always see the bad surrounding them. It is partly why the shadow is formed in the first place; the minds aren't yet developed to coherently understand why something has happened to them, and this becomes internalized.

It is only when they are older that it comes to light. Many parents, in fact, who take out negative feelings on their children have their shadows haunting them. Many children tend to trigger these reactions unintentionally and because the parents haven't done their internal reflection, it causes problems further down the road. It is usually common knowledge that people who bully were often bullied themselves, all part of the vicious cycle of abuse and trauma that sort of draws in the victim due to familiarity. Shadow work is great for breaking the vicious cycle and it will help bring out the inner child's ability to thrive creatively and use their institution more. It creates a strong trust within yourself.

The Inner Child

This prompt is so that you can familiarize yourself with the inner child that lurks beneath in your subconscious. Getting to know them will be an important step to unlocking your sense of adventure and lighthearted behaviors. The sort that encourages joy.

## Date:

1. What did you do for fun as a child?

2. What were your daydreams about?

3. Describe a time where you felt misunderstood as a child.

4. During your earlier school years, what was your daily routine like?

5. Who did you admire as a child (fictional or non-fictional)?

6. Where did you think you would be in the future, how does that relate to the life you have now?

7. What were your hobbies or extracurricular activities as a kid? Which ones did you enjoy, which ones did you stop and why?

8. If you could choose to take up any of these hobbies again which one would it be?

9. What was your favorite toy as a child and what was so significant about it?

10. Was there a time when you were unable to voice how you felt?

11. Is there someone in your life to whom you can speak your truth?

12. What are the boundaries you'd like to set up and be respected by people?

# Writing Prompts: The Inner Child

# Writing Prompts: The Inner Child

# Writing Prompts: The Inner Child

# Writing Prompts: The Inner Child

# Knowing When Your Inner Child is Wounded

"Most survivors grew up too fast. Their vulnerable child-selves got lost in the need to protect and deaden themselves. Reclaiming the inner child is part of the healing process. Often the inner child holds information and feelings for the adult. Some of these feelings are painful; others are actually fun. The child holds playfulness and innocence the adult has had to bury," - Laura Davis.

Since the inner child is the innocent, joyful, and playful persona, it can become reformed into an adult that struggles to say no and becomes a people pleaser, which is a bad thing since this is usually a recipe for people who abuse others' boundaries. Since there is no firm "no" from you, it can create disappointment in your daily life.

There are few signs that point towards a wounded inner child, and they are:

- Reactions towards situations based on previously experienced trauma. You can ask yourself a few questions concerning your negative experiences and answering them could potentially give you clarity on the situation. Did you feel like you were safe, loved, or as if you belonged in your family dynamic? If not, why? What sort of events made you feel as if your space wasn't safe?

- Relationships play a big part in how your internal monologue is crafted, and as previously mentioned, the shadow and inner child states can have a tremendous impact on it. We as people can be quite reactionary, or defensive, so don't be shy to inspect and observe the way you act around the people in your lives. It can be family members, friends, and even co-workers or, and sometimes especially, your boss. Sometimes the people that trigger us most are the authority figures in our lives, their behavior, and actions towards us can cause triggered regression and should be minded in case we have been carrying trauma gained from parents who are by all accounts the first authority figures in our lives.

- Noting our inner child's balance is no easy feat since a wounded child causes dissent. It can create too much child-like behavior, not highlighting a good balance of fifty/fifty external projection. Questions to ask yourself about inner child balance include: Are you in control of your emotions? Do you fear abandonment? Are you comfortable in your body?

## How to Heal Your Inner Child

"Where is that inner child that used to love so much? It's time to reconnect...Happiness and success depend on the child that you still carry within," - Roxanna Jones.

Simply knowing your inner child is wounded is the first step to the healing process. But how do you go about learning to heal your inner child? There are a few steps and suggestions to follow in order to help you through the process and advance the progress. After we have acknowledged the inner child and the shadow, the two personas will integrate into a better, newer you. To accept your inner child, it is key to remember that the inner child should be seen, heard, and loved. The inner child needs reassurance and tips to establish that reassurance includes grounding yourself and repetition of affirmations.

- Everything is ok, we are not in danger; you are safe; you are loved, I love you; you're going to be fine; what do you need from me?

- You want to use these parts as a way to integrate the two personas, take all the painful wounds and experiences, and unify them.

- A good affirmation to repeat to yourself is: I am loved. I am honored. I am free and it is done.

Uncovering

Use these prompts to uncover and declare your truth and to uncover who in your life are the people that respect you. Answer them without thinking too hard, let the child use their voice to show you what they are thinking, and then listen to them.

## Date:

1. If you could say anything to the antagonists in your life, you would say...

2. You can be yourself around...

3. It's ok to say no to people when...

4. You are ok with helping people when...

5. You can be the most vulnerable around...

6. You find it difficult to forgive people who...

7. You can easily forgive people who...

8. You think a fair boundary is...

9. You think an unfair boundary is...

10. Your expectations are valid because...

11. You feel cared about when someone gives you a...

12. What is your love language?

# Writing Prompts: Uncovering

# Writing Prompts: Uncovering

# Writing Prompts: Uncovering

# Writing Prompts: Uncovering

*Affirmation: To find fulfillment and acceptance, I need to look within.*

# Reparenting the Child

As part of the healing the wounded child method, there is a sub-theory that is referred to as re-parenting, when a professional takes the place of a parent over their patient and reestablishes the trust the child self needs in order to grow into a fully-fledged adult. This doesn't mean you can't re-parent yourself, it just means that trusting someone who is trained in these matters to handle that additional burden that is even too heavy for you to carry is often recommended. The point behind this re-parenting technique aligns with the identification of the wounded child. In our developmental stages, our parents were supposed to teach us a few crucial skills: Compassion, respect, self-esteem, emotional management, and crucial communication skills. When our parents aren't present, we lose out on these and are forced to either pick it up along the line, or instead, learn from them, which normally ends badly, as it leads to bad habits. So, when we enter the state of re-parenting, we understand that time cannot be reversed, and now it's time for that missing part of our lives to be filled. It's important to understand that while you want your parents to finish the job they started, or to even acknowledge where they lacked in your upbringing, it rarely happens and can only breed resentment towards them. Resentment is an emotion we are trying to avoid as it throws a wrench in your progress (Parent Co., 2017).

Shadow work is a more elaborate form of re-parenting and while it has similarities, the method of this chapter is more of an isolated experience. Whether you are using yourself or a psychologist, you need to understand that this is an act that must be contemplated. It's making sure you instill your child with the skill that your original parents couldn't help you with. You also need to watch out for developing an unhealthy codependent relationship with the therapist or yourself, as that can easily make you lose control. There needs to be clear boundaries and authority involved to prevent the inner child from taking over the core persona and to understand that this straightforward process is there for you to teach yourself independence.

So what steps does re-parenting include? It's all about giving yourself the affection you didn't receive as a child, and while it's no replacement for what you should have experienced as a child, re-parenting is the perfect moment for you to seize back the power that was denied to you.

This might feel a bit odd to you at first, especially if you had parents who weren't the best example to you, but this will be an experience that will remove those thoughts keeping you back.

You might think, how affectionate can you be with a child, there is only so much leniency you can provide to bad behavior, right? In fact, you might not even feel fit to be a parent to yourself. I'm here to tell you that there is nothing to fear. You know yourself the best, and the affection you will provide is going to be exactly what the inner child needs. What is the definition of affection? Simply put, it's the action that gives off warmth and comfort and the feeling that provides the most sense of safety. The best way I can describe it is when you were a kid and afraid and you threw your covers over your head and felt safe from all outside dangers, affection is much better than that. It's a hug in a moment of anxiety and feels like it is squeezed out of you. I think it's important to treat your child as someone almost separate when confronting them You can look at them with an unbiased eye, a difficult task but it will produce the best fruit for your labor.

You want to give the child as much positivity as possible while still establishing boundaries between you as the 'parent' and them as the child. Give yourself some treats; I like to write myself post-notes with small encouraging messages on them and stick it all over my home. It's nice because it gives you a reason to smile for the day. Embrace the joy, act in kindness, and you will see the child's fear dissipate and a new curious, wondering child will eventually emerge ready to live fearlessly.

Being the Parent

As you assume the role of parent, the child needs to separate from you in order for you to be able to nurture it. I will give you a few prompts to get the conversation going. You are going to be studying the inner child and who they represent to you. Treat the child how you would have liked to be treated.

## Date:

1. Take a moment and let the child materialize in your mind. How do you think the child is feeling? How does this make you feel?

2. What is that child in need of? Does the child feel like they are being judged?

3. Does the child feel shame?

4. Is the child expressing any experiences that were unpleasant? What would you want to tell the child?

5. As the parent, what is something you think the child deserves to hear?

6. Are you angry with the child? Let them know why, but be gentle about it.

7. Is your anger directed at the child or the people that hurt the child?

8. Talk about a person in our life that was supposed to be there for you, who let you down.

9. Do you feel as if you failed yourself and the child within?

10. If so, ask the child for forgiveness, and then take that step to reconcile with the child.

11. Listen to what the child has to say and write down what you think they would be telling you.

12. Sign off the chapter by reassuring the child that they are safe, they are loved, and they are valid.

# Writing Prompts: Being the Parent

# Writing Prompts: Being the Parent

# Writing Prompts: Being the Parent

# Writing Prompts: Being the Parent

Use this space to write your younger self a letter, think of the things you would have liked to hear when you were a kid, give them encouragement and hope. The letter should help you get clarity on your life and the past you led. It might be uncomfortable to put yourself in a regressive state; I like to think back to when I was at my lowest as a kid and then I visualize the way a scene should have played out in my head. You want to bring comfort to that small person inside you and it's important for you to give them that reassurance needed to get up again and feel strong. You've made it this far, so there is still hope, and don't despise the despair they felt when they were in the moment there was an escape for them. There is freedom. Maybe if you got away from a bad environment, detail to them the journey, highlighting that while it was a struggle, the results were that of freedom.

**Date:**

# Writing Prompts: Letter to the Child

# Writing Prompts: Letter to the Child

# Writing Prompts: Letter to the Child

# Writing Prompts: Letter to the Child

"As I continued letting my right hand know what my left hand was doing (and vice versa), I could feel the split within me begin to heal. The conscious and unconscious, the rational and intuitive, the thinking and feeling sides of my inner world began to embrace each other. In times of inner conflict, I turned to this wondrous process. It always brought clarity and insight. It always left me feeling better," - Lucia Capacchione.

# PART THREE:

# UNLOCKING YOUR CREATIVITY THROUGH INTEGRATION

You've gone over the hardest parts of the shadow work odyssey, like Greek hero Odysseus. It is time to return home and reclaim what was once yours. You battled the monsters, avoided the sirens, and narrowly avoided being turned into a pig by a Circe. Your child and shadow are Penelope, awaiting your return, and even though you have aged, and your appearance is different, you are still, by essence, your old self. The reunion of these two is the symbolism for when you become your full self and help push for wholeness. To reiterate, you need to make sure you follow the steps needed to encourage unification. Steps such as:

- **Accepting the Past**: Stifled memories that we avoid and can't be controlled need to be brought into the light despite if that makes us feel uncomfortable. When we do partake in this process, it's important to be aware of our triggers and not push ourselves so much that we lose sight of the important task. The positive note to this step is that it means when the past resurfaces in our daily lives, it's no longer so impactful in its outward and emotional force. Now we can finally grab hold of the bad thoughts, process them, and let them go. By accepting what we cannot change, we can let go and forgive for the sake of ourselves.

- **Dissect your current life choices based on the past's influence**: One of the most humbling experiences is realizing that other people are inherently broken, including the authority figures we were raised with. Dissecting your behavior and comparing it to others helps you understand that everyone has a shadow, and it gives that near-unconditioned compassion needed to make the right choices for ourselves and offer grace to those who hurt us. It's by no means a reason to let them back in your life since many people who are the way they are because of generational cycles won't always be able to heal. But your healing and breaking that cycle is the right move. We can't change the past, but we can change the way we perceive it.

- **Connecting the dots**: Many people suggest meditation as a way to center your mind to get it in a space that creates serenity. This you can do in many ways and is important for the convergence of self. For example, an alternative to meditation can be putting on some calm instrumental music so that your mind gets cleared and you can start to align all your thoughts into a more coherent zone. In the zone, you will be able to bridge the gap between the inner child and shadow. This harmonic connection will unlock the individualism within.

To keep up this process of authenticity, just remember to keep your journaling up to date and never lose sight of all the progress you've made. Your hard work will pay off, and even if you can't see that now, eventually, if enough time has passed, the image will become clear, and the healing will slowly start showing results.

## The Basics of Creativity

"The world always seems brighter when you've just made something that wasn't there before," - Neil Gaiman.

The next part is vital to your emotional growth. I know I have said that all the other steps are important, but this is too. Truth be told, none of the steps we have gone over is any less important than the other. All these parts make up a complete story. Your story, my story—the well-being of your mind and the history of your identity. The inner child and shadow might be two separate counterparts of each other, but they can work together as a unit. Therefore, part three of the book is so important. You have the puzzle pieces organized, color-coded, and ready to be packed. The remaining question is how? How are you going to merge yourself, the shadow, and the child into a full entity? By being creative and participating in some healthy escapism. In the next few sections, I will go over what you need to do to unlock that unified force sleeping beneath the surface, and how to embrace individualism and freedom of expression beyond society's expectations. If you have heard of Friedrich Nietzsche and his theories on the rejection of unrelated moral standards and societal values, then his story on the Camel, Lion, and Child is the perfect manner in which you can observe the full integration of oneself.

Part three is the crescendo in the symphony, the moment the build-up breaks, and the conductor sets loose a beautiful mix of noise that played together creates an unforgettable song. This is your song, and if you want to find your tune, let me take you on one more journey so that once you are ready, you can finally stand on your own, and become the assertive person you've always needed to be.

Creativity is a fundamental part of human life. While we do not always see it as the most important skill, it contributes to our overall mental wellbeing and provides a healthy escape in everyday life. Often seen as the illogical brain function, creativity is so much more than this. We like to package the expression of self as obnoxious, or as a waste of time, but in reality, it's this freeing experience and oftentimes its use is diminished. Society has a belief that in order to thrive, we have to block this crucial manifestation of self in favor of the typical cardboard life. Excessive use of colors and the portrayal of abnormal behaviors can cause this sense of judgment from other people. The truth of the matter is, that creativity is extraordinarily important to the art of healthy escapisms and self-reflection, which does not mean that working a 9-5 job is a bad thing or liking neutral colors makes you boring, that's not at all what I'm implying. I simply say that in order to be ourselves, we should express ourselves and break free from the constricted thoughts that want us to be constrained to certain behaviors. What is the expression, though? At its root, expression is making your thoughts and feelings known, and with the writing prompts, that is exactly what you have been doing. Bringing your thoughts and feelings to light, you are removing the negative power that binds it in your subconscious. I cannot express enough just how important this search for freedom is. The best part is, you don't have to be an artist to be expressive. It's in the finer details that you truly shine. Never forget that.

Being 'artistic' might be the traditional view of creativity, but it is by no means the only way you can unlock your inner self. Creativity can be expressed and expanded upon through so many varieties of hobbies, jobs, and everyday activities. Strangely enough, this also includes mathematics, a subject seen as boring by the majority of people. Matter-of-factly, mathematics was developed by dreamers and like-minded people who enjoy thinking of alternative solutions to complex problems. Math shadow work! Incredibly, something as simple as an outfit you picked out in the morning can be a way to bring therapeutic relief. Personally, I know of people who like to mismatch their socks, which gives them an extra spring in their step for the day. If you are stuck in a cubicle all day, adding personalized pictures around you, or a tiny house plant, can be that breath of fresh air away from the mental shackles that haunt you. Humans are complex. If we were simple creatures, then we wouldn't need to constantly look inside our deepest thoughts and wouldn't be subject to change as much as we are every day. The beauty of this complexity is that we are unique, and when our shadow self is integrated with the inner child, we are truly authentic and can finally break free of the shackles of suppression.

With an integrated persona, you'll soon realize just how important it is to have that authenticity in your life. The truth will set you free, and what is creative expression but the self-actualization and representation of who you are? You might finally be able to build up the confidence to set boundaries against people who only serve to create toxicity in yourself, and if you have any self-sabotaging behaviors, those will become less controlling over you because now that mindset of constant victimhood changes as you finally accept your shadow as not another, but instead as a part of yourself.

Victimhood, I hear you say, probably asking such a statement, means what? Well, let me elaborate and start by saying that in no way am I saying that any experience you have suffered over the years is directly your fault. Many times, these things happen to us and they are out of our control, which is a horrible experience, knocking us back a few steps in our life. This automatically makes us victims of circumstances, and in some ways, we will always be victims. That doesn't mean we can't reclaim our victimhood and turn it into something empowering. Negative thoughts are usually the root cause of the paralyzing effect victimhood can have on us, and it can stunt your growth as a person, which in turn pushes you right back into the darkness. As you can remember, one of the risks of shadow work is that a trigger can be too intense for you to process all at once, which is why you should have a professional constantly advising you and observing your progress so that when they see you're spiraling, you've got an anchor keeping you grounded. The best way to combat those thoughts that revert you to a victim state is to reaffirm them with positive thoughts. For example:

- I am inadequate—I am enough

- I am pathetic—I am strong

- I lack kindness—I am compassionate

- I am hated—I am loved.

These are just a few examples of how you can train your mind to think beneficially to feel assured by yourself that you are good enough. Another tip I find useful is that you can take this exercise and branch out with it, by answering why, after you've added the positive thought over the combating negative.

For example: I am loved because; my friend gives me little treats to say thank you sometimes, which gives me warmth and peace for the rest of my day.

You can even use this as a continuous writing exercise.

We all want love and the feeling of belonging, and by finding that niche, pulls us into our happy space, allowing us to find a loving community alongside it. I haven't spoken about reinvention and community yet, but I thought that before we speak about expanding upon your own personal creativity, it would be an excellent opportunity for me to broach the subject around a support system and joining and building a great community that can act as your outward positive environment. As a disclaimer, however, I want to add that there are pros and cons to joining a community of your choice, but I feel like it is one of those cases where the pros outweigh the cons. You need social interactions, and with the internet, your possibilities are endless, depending on your interest. It is filled with social media sites that encourage you to belong. From photography, poetry writing, or even blogging, the world naturally becomes your oyster and you the pearl. By surrounding yourself with people who share an interest in your hobbies and ways of relieving stress, you will be creating a temporary safe space of expression for yourself with others. Sharing and talking about these hobbies will lighten up your mind and heart, giving you that lost sense of belonging. It's a fantastic way to get to know people and practice your self-reflection.

This project and journaling steps are there to encourage belonging. You will see at the end of your journey how much growth has happened for you. It is good to gain perspective now and then. The best part is that now there is an open stage for you to not only contribute inwardly but also outwardly, and through self-acceptance, you can finally accept others.

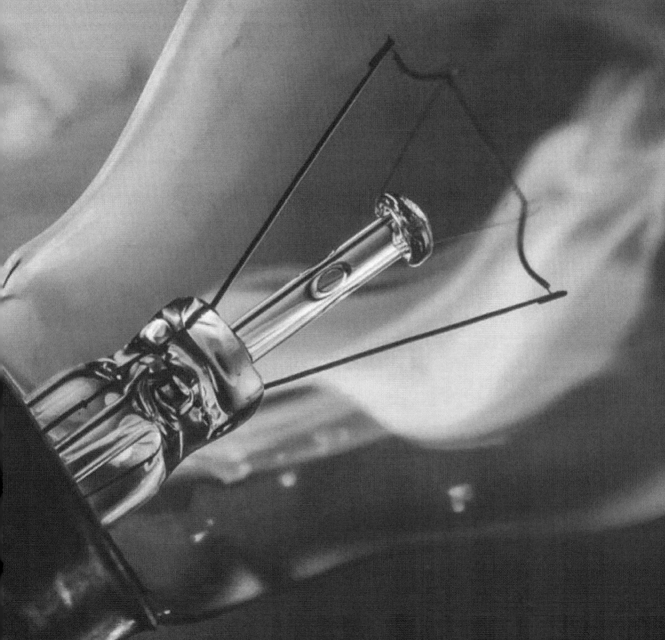

# What is Your Niche and How to Combat Victimhood

How can you contribute to your creative expression and freedom of self? In this next part, I want you to reflect upon what activity of expression gives you the best feeling of joy and freedom, but also how you can escape the choking negative thoughts that continuously put you in a bad mental space by using your own affirmative contributions to your own self.

## Date:

1. You feel the most energized when...

2. You are happiest when you...

3. You feel most creative when...

4. You feel like your higher purpose could be...

5. You feel your most comfortable in clothes that...

6. Your favorite color is...

7. The people who represent love in your life are...

8. You feel most heard when...

9. Your favorite form of affection is...

10. Nature represents...

11. Your home is your...

# 12. Your best version is...

# Writing Prompts: What is Your Niche and How to Combat Victimhood

# Writing Prompts: What is Your Niche and How to Combat Victimhood

# Writing Prompts: What is Your Niche and How to Combat Victimhood

# Writing Prompts: What is Your Niche and How to Combat Victimhood

*Affirmation: I am unique and my best self when I let go to express who I am.*

Your destiny is your own.

# Expanding on Your Inner Creativity

"There is no doubt that creativity is the most important human resource of all. Without creativity, there would be no progress, and we would be forever repeating the same patterns,"

- Edward de Bono.

When we are creative and we use our minds to go into that space, it can make us incredibly vulnerable, which is a good thing because the space you create in your own mode of creative expression is safe. You need that space to let loose and be yourself, which is an invaluable asset in your everyday life. It takes immense energy to pack away parts of yourself that might cause sachem. Compartmentalizing our disowned sides causes that restraint from fully living in the now and perpetuates crippling fear. There is a scene we are all quite familiar with, which is the moment an artist takes the paint, scooping it up haphazardly with brushes and splatters it with all their might across a blank canvas, or even an image they had already created. It's that sense of unadulterated feeling, where you can do no wrong because you are just taking it out on the blank canvas, forming it, and shaping it into something unique, organic, and frighteningly beautiful. I talk from experience, it's an exercise to try. Get some paints and a canvas or a piece of paper and just have at it. Use the colors you are immediately drawn to and make that jumbled-up picture because, in the end, it's you. Completely you. Not a reflection of a mirror staring back at you, manipulated with light, but a colorful splatter of you. You can take that abstract piece and hang it somewhere or paint it clean again and reuse it when you need to vent out that energy.

Another reason this moment can happen is when the artist already had a picture there, almost always a symbolic sign that the picture they have crafted for themselves didn't make them happy anymore. As compared to your subconscious mind, you picked up this book because you weren't happy with your picture. You needed to be taught to repaint and reassess it again, even if it is just a steppingstone in your overall adventure. You see, creativity or an accompanying hobby is what makes us human. We can have the numbers and rationality live our lives and use these "life lessons" to escape people's ire, but that doesn't guarantee us happiness, and the world loves to sell the idea of happiness to us in a perfectly commercialized package. From the fast-food adverts to the classy alcohol lifestyles, we are constantly supposed to accept this external pressure to be joyful. True happiness comes from knowing you were true to yourself, despite what you were surrounded by.

But how do you expand on your creativity and unlock the inner potential that nests there? What are the key steps to take? One step is integration between the child and the shadow. I touched on this briefly, but I thought I'd give a quick overview of this very important step in the next paragraph.

So, as we now know, each of us carries a shadow, and that shadow reflects inadequacy, shame, and guilt; things we gained from negative experiences in our early stages of life. It is coupled with the repression of things such as sexuality, fear, and bad thoughts, but we have moved on from that thought process and have learned that the shadow is our friend who needs love, just like us. I thought I'd take the opportunity to use expression and artistic wiles to unlock the good and bad thoughts and turn them into brilliant and free abstract thoughts. You've heard of Friedrich Nietzsche, the famous nihilist that everyone liked to follow. Well, he too ascribed to a similar theory of self-actualization, and if you follow each step correctly, you'd eventually reach the inner child and become fully actualized.

"We are like shop windows in which we ourselves are constantly arranging, concealing, or illuminating our supposed qualities, which others ascribe to us—all in order to deceive ourselves,"

- Frederick Nietzche.

In his book, *Thus Spoke Zarathustra*, Nietzsche describes a three-part metamorphosis we must all go through to reach that enlightenment.

The Camel, which is the 'spirit' that carries the heaviest of burdens describes those who are strong enough to take the steps into self-actualization, but can oftentimes get stuck in that stage of metamorphosis. I see this as the equivalent of the shadow's relationship with you as a person. Many times, we get stuck in the confrontation stage, where instead of sealing our wounds and moving on, we make them increasingly worse (Gambardella, 2020).

"There are many things for the spirit, for the strong heavy spirit in which dwell respect and awe: Its strength longs for the heavy, for the heaviest […] thus it kneels like the camel and wants to be well-laden,"

- Friedrich Nietzche.

These words reflect how the Camel acts, while the metaphor might sound strange as it explains the early phases of gaining new knowledge. We're not perfect, us humans, but it represents that thirst to learn and to store away all we have absorbed. Because we are strong as the Camel, we start burdening it with information and knowledge. We want to make sure we have enough of it all to survive the anguish and turmoil threatening to burst from our chests. We do things like reading, writing, traveling, and uncover the latest trinket in our lives. And the weight of all this knowledge weighs heavier and heavier, eventually, much to our dismay, we realize that we are still exactly where we were before because what is information if we don't use and adapt to it? Burnout is real, and it is dangerous because it can easily draw you back to the dark place, even if the dark place is just a terrified version of yourself.

The Lion is the second phase of the metamorphosis. The Camel, when unchanged, risks the chance of becoming bitter, lonely, and filled with despair. It doesn't help to have all the information and no way to expel that—this is where the Lion makes its appearance. "King of the Beasts," the Lion establishes its law over the land. When the Camel ventures out of the comfort of its space and heads off into the desert, which, according to Nietzsche, is humanity's expectation of the person you are, it's at this moment that the Lion truly realizes there is no limit to who you can be. In a place where everything is permitted, what are the things holding you back?

The "God is Dead" theory is often misrepresented here when it is just stating that there is no higher power dictating your decisions, and instead it is entirely up to you and your own free will (Raynor, 2016).

"God is dead. God remains dead. And we have killed him, - Fredrich Nietzsche.

This is where the connection to victimhood really ties in. It sounds unfortunate, but the Lion proves that your only limit is yourself. We spend many years thinking we are chained to societal pressures that torment us, but the truth is, you were always free. It's in the desert of the human condition where the Lion boldly exclaims, "I will," a stark contrast to the Dragon, the image of societal norms, who states quite boldly, "Thou Shalt." It's a form of rejecting permission and becoming a non-conforming entity of the moral laws and societal values that try to force us into a box. You are an organic shape, to be molded by your individualism, not to be forced into a shape you never were. These are the basic thoughts behind self-expression and acceptance. It's how you start to integrate your pieces. You are the masterpiece.

Finally, there is the child. You have fought hard to be the strongest, the freest, now it's time to settle down and begin anew. In the inner child chapter, I had you go over some writing prompts that lays your hurt and pain down, leaving it behind for a brighter clearer future. The child signifies your rebirth, a new beginning. While the Lion exemplified "NO," the child affirms life with an astounding "YES." By rejecting all that came before, your shape is new and ready to rebuild from the ground up. You can become someone entirely new with the same essence. That's what this is all about: Your own personal essence. Who you are when no one is looking and hopefully through this process, you realize you are an extraordinarily complex and unique person who deserves love, compassion, and kindness.

"For the sport of creation: The spirit now wills its own will, … its own world,"

- Friedrich Nietzche.

Your destiny is your own.

This might seem like it's a tangent away from creative expression, but this ties in quite nicely with my original points. I'd argue that Nietzsche was never a nihilist, as he has been famously miscast, but someone who grew tired of the bonds of society and its expectations on the way to act. They will try at everything to wring individualism out of you. Being different is bad. Being different is awkward. Let me let you in on a secret. We are all human at our core with genuine acceptance. True individualism is when you embrace every single flaw, weird quirk, and even bad behavior you have picked up over the years, move on, grow, and let go. Therefore, creative expression is so crucial. I thought I would leave a few options for you to pick from, a way to branch out your individualism to not only yourself but to the world.

1. Take a look at the story of the Camel, Lion, and Child, and make a visual interpretation of the journey these three characters had to take to actualize their true selves. Attribute yourself to this journey. You can use anything from photography to painting. Even taking something as simple as play-doh to make a sculpture can be a good design. Record this in your workbook as a reference for later.

2. Another idea that could be fun and reflective is to draw, paint, or write in the dark. It's a good way to get an idea of how it feels to be a shadow suppressed and not in the light. After you've done this, turn on the light and start turning your creation into something subjectively beautiful. Add an animal or flower that brings significance to your life and applies to the concept of rebirth.

3. Create a collage of images that draws your attention, don't focus too much on what they are and what they represent yet. Just let them draw your attention. You can use Pinterest to make a Pinboard if you don't have access to physical materials, making what we refer to as a mood board. After you have selected a few pictures that genuinely speak to you, take a moment to study them, write what they mean to you, and how that ties in with your journey.

4. Watch a movie from your childhood that you loved and write about how it has influenced you.

5. Keep a dream journal. This suggestion might seem a bit cliche, but many artists have had their best ideas and reflective moments over dreams. They aren't some deeply spiritual experiences, your dreams are usually tied to your subconscious, so it is the perfect way to keep track of what you are going through.

6. Make a sculpture of your hand in plaster and write all the wonderful qualities about yourself on it. As a way to imply that you're the master of your destiny and destination.

7. Remember to have fun and join a community. If you enjoy reading, join a book club. If you enjoy painting, join a hobbyist paint group. There are a few people who enjoy the calming qualities of nature. It's a space where you can feel at ease away from the noise.

8. Write the negative three words you associate with yourself and then write their opposites down next to it. How does it make you feel?

9. Expressing what hobbies give you the best freedom to be yourself and do something as an example. For example, write a poem, do a collage/mood board, draw or take a picture of your favorite outfit.

10. Take the above prompt and write your thought process around why you chose that specific form of expression.

11. Come up with your own personalized affirmation.

12. After you've done that, take your affirmation and go do something fun with it. Maybe embroider it on a pillow? Make it something visible to you most of the time.

**Date:**

# Writing Prompts: Express Yourself

# Writing Prompts: Express Yourself

# Writing Prompts: Express Yourself

# Writing Prompts: Express Yourself

Using your newfound creative inspiration, write a letter to yourself 10 years into the future. Really note down where you want to be emotionally, physically, and in your career path. Take a moment to visualize where you want to be in the next few years, create that space to live in and to experience, then write the letter with all that in mind. Thank your future self for getting this far, for being willing to go through all the heartache and hurt in order to thrive to their better selves. Acknowledge the struggles they might have come across and the relationships that had to change. Like with the child, reassure them that all of this is a temporary stop and that you are sure they ended up doing the right things for themselves. Maybe even tell them how excited you are that you can finally take the steps to your progression, and that you're excited to see your story unfold. Be bold, be brave, and always be authentic to who you are. When you find yourself reading the letter again, you will have the perfect story to treasure as you walk into your life with a lighter, informed step. This is your narrative that you have created, and this letter, as well as those before, prove that it's all in your control now, no one else can have the power over you again. With this final letter, I know you will become empowered.

**Date:**

# Writing Prompts: Letter to the Future

# Writing Prompts: Letter to the Future

# Writing Prompts: Letter to the Future

# Writing Prompts: Letter to the Future

"What we call the beginning is often the end. And to make an end is to make a beginning. The end is where we start from,"
- T.S Elliot.

# CONCLUSION

I'll admit, ending this book is quite difficult for me, and I'm sure, in a way, now that its pages are filled with your soul, you too feel that loss. The good news is, while I am moving on, you still have a complete story to tell, and this is hardly the end. It's your beginning. We have cried, we have laughed, and we have grieved. Take courage, there is a beauty beyond your pain, and like the phoenix, you will rise from the ashes and be born anew. You are an independent, strong, and wonderful person who has been shaped by negative experiences and no longer controlled. You are not alone. This book is a personal project for many, and just because my words end at the end of the book, your words will live on in more journals and more artistic endeavors. I know that while you have suffered, there's renewed hope that your light was never lost and has always been there. Share it. It is a shame to hide someone as incredible as you in an isolated instance.

They always say goodbyes are the hardest. Personally, I think it's the strength to continue fighting and living that is the hardest part. A goodbye is final. The fight is ongoing, but even that will come to its end one day. I'll leave you with this: Be the best you. Don't let anyone define who you are and who you are going to be. Be assertive in who you are and let yourself make mistakes, encouraging grace to yourself because you can only learn from those mistakes. Give yourself a break now and then, don't let the guilt control you. Some days we need a lazy day in order to reset ourselves. Every day doesn't have to be about work, relationships, and self-improvement. Self-love is also knowing when all you need is to curl up in your bed and sleep like the dead. Do you enjoy reading? Do that. Video games? No problem. Escapism is good for you. Draw and write those stories, find your love language, whatever you need, it's ok to be just a bit selfish sometimes. I'm not saying hide forever, but grant yourself the privilege of a moment's rest, the world will still be there when you come back. It's not going anywhere. Not yet anyway.

I hope this has been enlightening, and I hope that you have found the peace within yourself to move to greater and better things. You are loved. Good luck.

# AUTHOR BIO

Victoria Stevens is the author of several Self-Help books.

Victoria's interest in childhood trauma and development began very early in her life. Since childhood she was verbally and emotionally abused by her highly manipulative and authoritarian parents, which brought her enormous suffering.

Victoria found herself approaching life disheartened because of her parents' effect on her self-confidence and self-love and found herself living several stories and friendships, one more troubled than the other!

To the young Victoria the world felt a very unpredictable and unsafe place, but not being the kind of woman who gives up easily, Victoria decided to delve into the theories of developmental psychology and childhood trauma to try and alleviate the suffering she sees in herself and so many people.

Through her publications, Victoria has already helped thousands of people regain a healthy and successful self-image, healing their inner child, integrating all their inner parts living in the shadow, and achieve a sense of wholeness and freedom. Her daily practice has been heavily influenced by the scholarship of Carl Jung and many other well-renewed psychologists, psychotherapists, and physicians.

The author's mission is to share with as many people as possible her most effective methods for resolving inner issues through the famous method of "shadow work journaling workbook with prompts" and the "3 letters to Improve personal awareness and authenticity". These concepts represent her greatest discoveries and her most successful tools.

Victoria herself is also a nature enthusiast and loves to journal to feel connected to the world outside. She didn't grow up religious and wanted to find a way to bypass the usual religious idea behind self-improvement and healing. She wants to express that there are many alternatives to your journey that don't require meditation or religion. She wants this book to be something different and to reassess the fideistic approach to healing.

This is where her love for journaling and nature comes in handy as she uses these moments to record her thoughts and feelings. Always writing and reflecting on the moments in her life and wondering about where she is going. Victoria is a big enthusiast of analytical psychology and wants to use what she has learned to inspire others and most importantly, herself. Using the skills and research she has accumulated; she wants to make the most of her values and advance in her career as writer.

She knows that through deeper connections, everybody can lead a meaningful life. She strongly suggests the art of Shadow Work to work through insecurities such as past failures, loss, and grief. The use of these techniques can prevent them from spreading over to other people. When she is not at work, the author likes to spend time by the sea as it's her favorite place. From the serenity of the beach, where people can socialize and be joyful, to the unpredictable exciting ocean, life can often surprise you in the beauty it holds. It is no wonder that Victoria Stevens owns a sailboat, which she regularly takes out along the San Francisco Bay, where she can feel most at peace and in tune with herself.

Through this book, she hopes you can see her heart and vision beyond the ordinary and let it take you on a journey of growth and love. Fighting your insecurities along the way with her, and she knows you will get a life-changing experience from her books.

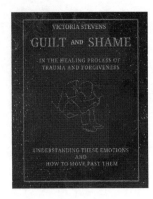

# YOUR FREE GIFT: GUILT and SHAME IN THE HEALING PROCESS OF TRAUMA AND FORGIVENESS. UNDERSTANDING THESE EMOTIONS AND HOW TO MOVE PAST THEM.

Dear reader, this is a free gift to you for placing your trust in my hands and for giving me the opportunity to guide you.

I want you to understand that you are carrying great power within you, and that there are many benefits and blessings associated with you doing Shadow Work. The greatest of all are finding a sense of purpose inside you and harmony all around you.

However, it is never easy to undertake this "solo" journey and you should always allow yourself plenty of time to fully process your memories and the feelings associated with them. This includes to stop reading and journaling for a while or seek professional help should you ever feel completely overwhelmed.

To maximize the value that you are going to receive from this book, I highly encourage you to join our tight-knit community on Facebook. Here you will be able to connect and share with other like-minded- Shadow Workers in our continuing path to growth. Taking this journey alone can be tricky, so this is an excellent support network for you. It would be great to connect with you there.

*Victoria Stevens*

>> Join Our Fb Group Self-Acceptance Through Shadow Work <<

Join a community of people that share a deep interest in doing accurate shadow work for real healing and increased self-awareness. A place where you can safely ask questions and interact with likeminded and respectful people. A group providing guidance, community and support. Expect also to be involved in promotions, give aways, freebies and information about new projects.

 yourshadowworks

yourshadowworks

*Facebook Page*
*Shadow Work Journal & Workbook*

victoriastevens@yourshadowworks.com

# WE'RE HERE BECAUSE OF YOU

If you have found any value in this material,
Please consider leaving a review and joining the Author's
Mission to bring more healing into this world
By scanning the QR-Code below ♥

Share a photo or video and write an honest review of your
Shadow Work Journal and Workbook

on **Amazon, TikTok or Instagram** to get the new digital

book (pdf) on **"Shadow Work for Self-Love"**

**worth $19,99, absolutely free $0**

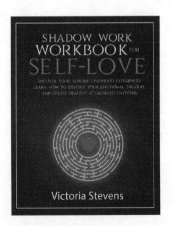

DM @yourshadowworks
email:

victoriastevens@yourshadowworks.com

with your link to receive your special

discount

*@yourshadowworks*

# REFERENCES

Arabi, S. (2018, June 6). What Is The Shadow Self? And How Do I Do Shadow Work? Thought Catalog. https://thoughtcatalog.com/shahida-arabi/2018/06/shadow-self-shadow-work/

Capacchione, L. (1991). Recovery of your Inner Child: The highly acclaimed method for liberating your inner self. (Illustrated). Touchstone. https://www.amazon.com/Recovery-Your-Inner-Child-Liberating/dp/0671701355

Centre of Excellence. (2019, September 16). What is Shadow Work? Centre of Excellence. https://www.centreofexcellence.com/what-is-shadow-work/

Emma. (2021, June 3). 33 Journal Prompts From a Seasoned Shadow Worker. Medium. https://medium.com/mystic-minds/33-journal-prompts-from-a-seasoned-shadow-worker-fc74ab962505

Ford, D. (2001). The Dark Side of the Light Chasers: Reclaiming your power, creativity, brilliance, and dreams. Hodder & Stoughton.

Fordham, F., & Michael S.M. Fordham. (2019). Carl Jung | Biography, Theory, & Facts. In Encyclopædia Britannica. https://www.britannica.com/biography/Carl-Jung

Fosu, K. (2020, December 14). Shadow Work: A Simple Guide to Transcending The Darker Aspects of The Self. Medium. https://medium.com/big-self-society/shadow-work-a-simple-guide-to-transcending-the-darker-aspects-of-the-self-e948ee285723

Gambardella, S. (2020, August 21). Nietzsche's three steps to a meaningful life. Medium. https://medium.com/the-sophist/nietzsches-three-steps-to-a-meaningful-life-f063793adfc4

Hall, M. P. (1980). Studies in character analysis: phrenology, palmistry, physiognomy, graphology, Oriental character analysis. Philosophical Research Society.

Inner Shadow Work Website. (2021, March 17). 30+ Powerful Affirmations for Shadow Work. https://innershadowwork.com/affirmations-for-shadow-work/

Jeffrey, S. (2019, April 15). Shadow Work: A Complete Guide to Getting to Know Your Darker Half. Osage. https://scottjeffrey.com/shadow-work/

Jung personality test. (2019). 123test.com. https://www.123test.com/jung-personality-test/

Liang, L. (2019, March 30). Three Metamorphoses: Camel, Lion, Child. Medium. https://counterreality.medium.com/three-metamorphoses-camel-lion-child-a0a184e15a06#:~:text=In%20Nietzsche

Martin Evan Jay. (2018). Sigmund Freud | Austrian psychoanalyst. In Encyclopædia Britannica. https://www.britannica.com/biography/Sigmund-Freud

Masterclass Staff. (2020, November 8). Writing 101: The 12 Literary Archetypes. Masterclass. https://www.masterclass.com/articles/writing-101-the-12-literary-archetypes#whats-the-difference-between-archetypes-stereotypes-stock-characters-and-clichs

Mcleod, S. (2018, May 21). Carl Jung | Simply Psychology. Simplypsychology.org. https://www.simplypsychology.org/carl-jung.html

Neill, C. (2018, April 21). Understanding Personality: The 12 Jungian... Moving People to Action; Conor Neill. https://conorneill.com/2018/04/21/understanding-personality-the-12-jungian-archetypes/

Owings, S. (2020, April 4). The 12 Literary Archetypes. Medium. https://medium.com/the-brave-writer/the-12-literary-archetypes-1e623ac06ca5

Paler, J. (2019, January 18). Shadow work: 8 steps to heal the wounded self. Hack Spirit. https://hackspirit.com/7-shadow-work-techniques-to-heal-the-wounded-self/

Parent Co. (2017, November 7). How a Parent's Affection Shapes a Child's Happiness for Life. The Gottman Institute; https://www.gottman.com/blog/how-a-parents-affection-shapes-a-childs-happiness-for-life/

Perry, C. (2015). The Shadow | Society of Analytical Psychology. Society of Analytical Psychology. https://www.thesap.org.uk/resources/articles-on-jungian-psychology-2/about-analysis-and-therapy/the-shadow/

Raynor, T. (2016, April 13). Nietzsche's Three metamorphoses. WordPress; Philosophy for Change. https://philosophyforchange.wordpress.com/2010/02/12/nietzsches-three-metamorphoses/

Regan, S. (2020, December 22). Meet Your "Shadow Self": What It Is When It Forms & How To Work With It. MBG Mindfulness. https://www.mindbodygreen.com/articles/what-is-shadow-work

Rosenberg, J. (2019). 90 Seconds To A Life You Love: How To Master Your Difficult Feelings To Cultivate Lasting Confidence, Resilience, And Authenticity. Little Brown Spark.

Russell, T. (n.d.). How to Get In Touch with Your Dark Side Through Shadow Work. Shape. Retrieved July 6, 2021, from https://www.shape.com/lifestyle/mind-and-body/mental-health/what-is-shadow-work

Schwartz, S. (2020, January 23). How a Parent's Affection Shapes a Child's Happiness | SPSP. Www.spsp.org. https://www.spsp.org/news-center/blog/schwartz-parents-children-affection

Seeking Serotonin. (2021, January 11). 31 Days of Shadow Work Journal Prompts For Healing and Growth. https://seekingserotonin.com/shadow-work-journal-prompts/

Sprankles, J. (2020, August 17). What Is Shadow Work? Scary Mommy. https://www.scarymommy.com/shadow-work/

Stein, C. (2019, February 14). 365 Creative Writing Prompts. ThinkWritten. https://thinkwritten.com/365-creative-writing-prompts/

Wikipedia. (2020, January 18). Shadow (psychology). https://en.wikipedia.org/wiki/Shadow_(psychology)

Wikipedia Contributors. (2019, March 4). Jungian archetypes. ; https://en.wikipedia.org/wiki/Jungian_archetypes

All Images are sourced from Pixabay